STROKE

THE ROAD BACK

Doris W. Braley

HARBOR HOUSE (WEST) PUBLISHERS

# DEDICATION

To Margaret Witten, R.N.,
She is the wind beneath my sails

BOOKS BY DORIS W. BRALEY

Now Is For All

Perfect Ending

ℱOREWORD

BY CHARLIE W. SHAEFFER, JR., M.D.

𝒟oris Braley, through her verse and prose, offers the reader a uniquely expressively insight into the complexities of the emotions of the stricken and recovering stroke patient.

A stroke is caused by a sudden obstruction to flow in a blood vessel supplying the brain. Its outcome, which is often fatal, is determined by the event location and segment of brain affected. It is the third most common cause of death in the United States, exceeded only by heart attack and cancer. It is the most common cause of permanent disability. This is likely the reason why many patients fear stroke as intensely or more than any other illness. A positive attitude and motivation to get well exhibited in this work is a critical success factor to recovery.

This first-hand account of Doris Braley's experience with this life-threatening illness will serve as an inspiration and support to stroke victims and their families.

TABLE OF CONTENTS

BOOK ONE: THE STROKE

$\mathcal{B}$OOK $\mathcal{T}$WO: THE ROAD BACK

Book One

THE STROKE

. . . AS WE BEGIN

*W*e cannot know God's Master Plan, but it's enough to be a part of it. Why am I using given talents that lay dormant, even abused, until now? How is it that I had not found myself before?

Was I too busy? Did I not care?

Think of the wasted years! I am near the end of my time and rather in awe of this exciting burst of energy that is proving to be such an opportunity to share my laughter, my tears, my sorrow and my love with you.

If this is God's invitation, I must willingly accept!

Please join me.

A Few Things You Should Know…

It may not do a lot of good to say this now, but I'm going to anyway.
I've been there and I think I may know how you feel.

Try to be patient in the days up ahead until you find out how severe your
stroke is. If one side is paralyzed, understand that often healing takes time.
It may not come in a hurry.

Don't worry about your speech right now. Don't push it. Don't try too soon.
Let others do all they want to do for you. You need to take time now to recover
from the trauma of your stroke. You must understand this.

Let's walk together through my notes my thoughts and my progress as I
fought my way — at times reluctantly or obstinately — through my stroke.
My prayer is that my ordeal may help you and your family — and along the
way, hopefully, you will come to understand that recovery is often possible as
we share my story, the poetry and the photographs that continue to emerge.

God gave me the tools to make the words and the pictures happen.
I believe He did this just so I could share them with you as we discover
The Road Back, together.

DAY ONE!

I backed away to get a better look at the lower shelf of the refrigerator where I had stored the vegetable oils for salad dressings. As I straightened up, I felt dizzy and my left leg became numb. When I tried to walk the leg collapsed and I found myself lying on the floor. Unable to get up. I called to my sister Susan, who half carried me to a chaise. My speech became slurred and confused. Susan called 911 first, then my doctor who said he would call the hospital and meet us in Emergency.

By the time he arrived, I had lost consciousness. There followed the usual X-rays, lab tests, blood work, Sonogram, C-Scan, and Angiogram.

I remember none of that.

POOR BIRD

I just laid there very still
not moving,
like a poor little bird with a broken wing.
Beak open, barely breathing,
but oh, so still,
so very still.

A day later, I regained consciousness. The lights in the hospital room were puzzling to me…they gave a pinkish glow to everything. I closed my eyes tight. When I opened them again, there was a nurse — bathed in the same pink light — smiling as she asked, "Do you know where you are?"

I tried to say, "Yes, Good Samaritan," but was terrified at the bumbling sounds that came from my lips. My husband, who stood beside the nurse, mirrored my terror in his eyes as he bent to kiss me. He too, looked pink.

As I tried to ask him what was wrong with me, again what came out of my mouth made no sense and when I reached for him to hold me, my left side refused to move.

I remember crying — not at all like me — I sounded like a wounded animal. As he held me close, telling me it would be all right, I became very frightened, because these words came out as his "whistling in the dark voice."

Then my doctor was there — people kept fading in and out — taking my blood pressure, asking me questions that I didn't try to answer for fear of hearing those garbled words coming out of me again. I could only whimper as I looked at him, my eyes pleading with him to do something. I felt devastated.

Dr. Long said, "Dode, you have had a stroke. Just put up with our testing you every once in a while and we'll see how long it will be before we can get you back to normal."

I had had a stroke to be sure. That probability had worried the doctors in the past for some time. My blood pressure had been very high, 250/150; my migraine headaches too frequent and too severe.

I had lost control over the left side of my body. My facial muscles drooped on the left and my left hand was like a poor little injured bird, unable to move. It was just there.

The words
They just wouldn't
Nor couldn't come.
I knew them,
What I needed to say,
But they couldn't come.
My tongue was dumb
My brain, numb…

My left side
It seemed to have died.
Leg and foot collapsed.
Hand useless.
Face drooped to the left
Eyes, vacant — bereft.

9

WHEN?

When will this confusion leave me?
When will I be myself again?
When will I be able to think again and give voice to what is on my mind?
When will others understand me?
When will they stop looking embarrassed?
Or sad?

DON'T GO

Don't go
    don't leave me,
    hear me out.
You sit there
    never moving,
    pretending rapt attention.
Or so it seems.

But your mind's
    a mile away.
You've forgotten
    you were going to stay
and listen
    to what I have to say
    even though it takes all day.

Come back,
    listen.
Hear me,
    please.

THE HARDEST PART

Perhaps, although it was for the shortest time, the fact that I couldn't speak was the hardest part of it all. I couldn't express myself. What came out was just garbled. How people would look at me, wondering if they would be able to interpret what I was trying to say. The nurses would almost will the words to my brain and then to my lips. This was all new to my family so they didn't know how to respond. But the nurses and doctors knew, and seemed to understand.

The nurses helped me learn how to talk again by speaking slowly, and if I said something that didn't come out as I had planned, they would say, "I think you meant to say this, Mrs. Braley." I responded, "You're right," or, "No!"

I was so mad for so long that there were many times I said "No" to everything. I seemed to dislike a lot of people who were trying to help me. I was just so mad at the world. I was so frustrated. And boy! Did I swear!

I was mad at the Lord. I loved Him so. Trusted Him so. Why did He let it happen? And when was He going to make it all right again?

INNER STRENGTH

Feeling God's presence you begin to
accept your losses with your head held
high, with the poise of a woman, not
the uncertainty of a child.

You make your plans for now because
you can't be sure that there will be a
tomorrow.

You learn that the earth doesn't turn for
you alone. That you must do your own
thing and help others too. That you
must wait patiently and Let God!

You'll discover you can survive. You
are well-versed, profound and strong.

And with every loss you learn.

DROP FOOT

One of the first days after my stroke, a board was put at the foot of my bed. A nurse worked my leg and taught me to push against the board. This was to begin to strengthen my left foot. At first I could hardly move my leg but with the repetition — three times a day — soon the foot began to respond. But slowly.

Can this be — The foot…that kicked the soccer goal?
        …that balanced on the beam in gym?
        …that mounted my horse?
        …walked the golf course?
        …climbed a hill to fly a kite?
        …danced all night?
Why won't it even try to simply walk now???

My thigh also became strong again from the movements in bed. But, when the time came to get my foot strong enough so I could walk again, I found they expected me to learn to use a walker. I detested a walker. I stayed with my wheelchair until I could, with some assistance, use a cane comfortably.

WALKING WITH NORA

*M*y night nurse, Nora, was also determined to help me progress. She worked my left foot against the end of the bed on a specially built pillow to strengthen the muscles. She had a plan to help me walk.

Nora put her hands on my upper arms and with me facing her, had me do the same with my good right hand. She told me to look down at her white shoes and when her right foot stepped back, I should follow it with my opposite one. Then when she stepped back with her left foot, I should follow that one with my right. That way we could walk to the bathroom and eliminate using the bedpan. GREAT!!!

It was drudgery and took a lot of effort to think it out at that point. It was a struggle to make my legs move, but I knew if I stayed with Nora's plan I would function again.

It was a task but it was my commitment to another person who cared about me. We would practice each night on Nora's shift. First a challenge, then it became an accomplishment. We laughed and hugged each other.

THE PROBLEM WITH PHYSICAL THERAPY

*M*y nurses were great. Especially the morning nurse, Linda. She knew I was disturbed about physical therapy and it wasn't doing me any good. When the PT delivery boy wheeled me into therapy, he would ask, "What about her?", pointing to me. The head guy would answer, "Oh, her. Walk her around the room again." My guy would say, "Okay, Mrs. B., let's try it again."

It reminded me of my dancing school days when all the handsome boys would pick the pretty blondes and I would end up with the short, pimply faced son of the teacher.

The therapist dragged me around, stumbling, once more and then put me back in my wheelchair.

PT was a real downer!

Seeing my distress each time I returned from these sessions, my nurse, Linda, made a decision. Telling no one, the next day she came on her shift in street clothes and was conveniently out of the room when the boy picked me up in the wheelchair to go to PT. When we passed her in the hall, she gave me a big wink and I saw she had a scarf over her head. I was confused (but at that time, that was an easy way to be!).

When we entered the exercise room I saw Linda sitting with all the wives and mothers. Bless her, she had dressed out of uniform because nurses are not allowed to come with patients and she was spying on those so called "professionals."

The doctor told me that Linda said I was not doing well in PT and he suggested I try Occupational Therapy instead.

I did. It worked. Ah, it worked.

OCCUPATIONAL THERAPY

*W*hen Linda wheeled me to Occupational Therapy she explained what they would do to, and for me. All three of my nurses had been working on my speech and I could say one or two words, so to be understood.

The therapist said "yes" when I asked, "Linda stay?" and I think that was the best, most assuring promise I had heard since my stroke. I had actually said words that were recognized and answered. I felt ten feet tall and knew Linda realized it too.

Two more women were wheeled in and I hurt for them. Jane's head hung down and she appeared to be asleep. There was no response when the Therapist spoke to her. She could move nothing.

The other one, Sara, seemed to hear but there was no reaction to the Therapist's voice. But when I said "Hi…Linda stay…me." Sara looked at me — right at me! Then stared at the floor, saying nothing.

The Therapist put hand lotion on we three and told us to rub it in all the way.

I rubbed it in to my poor left hand with the right, but couldn't reverse it because the left one just hung there.

Jane didn't move.

Sara just sat and stared at the lotion on her hands. I helped her with my good right hand, and later I wrote this:

SARA

Sara sat in her wheelchair
As I sat in mine.
She stared at the floor,
I studied her.
The nurse smeared lotion on our hands,
Urged us to rub it in.
Sara stared at the floor.
I helped her with my good hand — sort of guided her.
She lifted her head,
Eyes met mine to say thanks.
Then again —
Sara stared at the floor
As though to show me how to escape
This prison.

PRISON...FREEDOM

*L*earning that Occupational
Therapy had Arts and Crafts
for patients to use, Linda, aware I had
a background of painting, suggested I
try to express myself with a brush…
Herewith, my painting…

All the synonyms for anguish were
mine. I was hurting when I painted this
but held hope that there could be a life
once I broke out of my imprisonment.

With God's help, I no longer saw
bars at the window. They and the stones
disapperared, faded away, leaving water,
sky and clouds. I could even feel the
wet sand between my toes.

Lose those bars and your prison
falls away to freedom…despair turns
to hope!

So, trust God to help you help
yourself to hope again.

*O*nce in Occupational Therapy there was no one else — just Linda with me. The therapist covered my eyes with a cloth, opened my good hand and put some coins in it. Then she took them all out and put them back, one at a time. I had to tell her which one she had returned. I knew, but I couldn't say the name of each one. We did this every day and I improved as time went on. A miracle!

(I wish Sara had been there!)

Another day the therapist put materials in my hand; each one was different — rough then soft, then scratchy, slippery, hard, smooth, sticky, wet, very dry. I was suppose to identify each one. This helped me do three things: think hard, identify and try to remember. We did this procedure again and again. As a result I got better each time — knew the names of more materials as I worked at it. It took a lot of work, and some things I never did recall. But the therapy was a success. I took another step along the way.

When Linda learned I would have to climb stairs at my house, she attempted to help me use a walker in my room and in the halls. Early one morning she swung in with my wheelchair and said," We are going to try something new."

There were large closed stairwells at each end of the floor. The stairs were big, wide and long, but not too high. Linda wheeled me down the hall. "You are going to get out of the wheelchair now and practice climbing these stairs." I was really shocked but tickled to try something new, so I asked, "Do I have to unclimb them too?" "You bet," Linda said, laughing.

I climbed them twice a day, regaining strength and balance that I never thought possible.

PULL OF THE TIDE

You don't have to stand knee deep in water
To feel the pull of the tide.
You don't have to see the gulls swoop low,
Then soar on the wind's stately ride.
Just close your eyes, remember your dreams
Let them be your purposeful guide,
In the depth of your heart there'll always be part
That belongs to the pull of the tide.

RECOVERY AWAY FROM THE HOSPITAL

*W*hen it was time for me to leave the hospital, Linda and Nora came with me for each of their shifts.

They spoke again of the stairs as my husband carried me up them.

They discussed how we would have to work a little more each day on conquering them. It really helped that they started me walking the stairwell while hospitalized. Now it became a twice daily routine. After a week, it became three times a day. Some days it was so tiring, I felt exhausted, frustrated and wanted to quit only to have one of the nurses say, "Try it once more, and I want to see a big grin this time."

When I really had had it and felt nothing was worth the effort, I fell back on one of my Mother's pet expressions, "You go to grass!" This, said with the right amount of vengeance, usually bought some time to rest.

I slept a lot — didn't want to get dressed and still had no appetite. I had to be encouraged, almost forced to eat.

I didn't want to see or talk with friends or even family. I felt deeply depressed. All of a sudden the world was too much to handle.

When these periods hit me, it was usually after I had experienced a good day or even several days that were looking up. Then all at once I would withdraw.

NOT ENOUGH

What happened to me?
Was I so hypnotized
I could do anything?
Was I so fascinated that
I was charmed by everyone
and
they, by me?

Then the bloom was gone.
The doubts and pain were back.
The heartaches too.

You've become ambitious again
climbing again.
You really need someone
to bring your trophies to…don't you?

I'm still only me,
but that's not enough
…is it?

MY "IFFY" BODY

$\mathcal{I}$ often thought of myself as being imprisoned
in what I called my "Iffy Body!"

It's movements were erratic and unpredictable.
Even my thoughts were uncertain and oversensitive.
I was very negative.

I would plan ahead only to find on that special
day my back and legs would balk and give me intense
pain. Or I might have vertigo. Or my heart would be
unstable. And very often gastritis. Really many physical
things totally unlooked for and unexpected would be
the basis of disappointments which makes me call my
body "Iffy." If my body would stop throwing in these
ringers perhaps I could complete my recovery.

But, no — "Iffy" was, and is, a part of who I am.
(Even perhaps who I always will be.) I don't have to
like it, just learn to live with it.

GOOD DAYS AND BAD DAYS

There were good days and bad days.
Promising days and sad days.
Days of work — all uphill,
But days of song as I grew strong.

FEARS I HAD...

The greatest fear I had was having another stroke.

There were many times when I thought about giving up. Times when I was too depressed to try to do what the nurses and therapists had programmed for me, when all I wanted to do was put my head under the blanket…and withdraw. But this feeling I overcame through my strong willpower and faith.

Not wanting to see people was that old withdrawal business again. I didn't want to see friends, family, even my grandchildren. Without my family's love, caring and encouragement, I would never have made the road back. If you have these feelings too, don't feel badly or worry about it. This happens frequently but after a time these feelings will disappear and you will again enjoy being with family and friends. You will look forward to each of their visits.

Blaming God is again a frequent emotion. We should be glad He has such broad shoulders. If your faith in Him is strong, you'll have no trouble in believing that He will help you get well again and just be grateful that you can be so fortunate as to receive His love and vigilance at this difficult time.

THE CONSTANT BATTLE

How do I live between a rock and a hard place? A way that you,
God experienced so many times.
I hear criticism…
I hear ridicule…
I'm called a liar.

They don't realize it takes just plain guts for me to work as hard as
I do to bestow a presence that they can live with.
They think I am just indolent…
exaggerating my pain…my disappointments.

They know little of the ache in my heart as I try to make me seem
normal. They know nothing of the confusion behind everything I
try to do. Or the brave front I put up for their peace of mind rather
than let them know I am scared.

"Scared?" One wonders?…Then I think on You, oh God, and all my
fear and anxiety fall away as I become sure and strong. Your presence
reminding me, I will never be alone!

I had a dear friend, a psychiatrist, to whom I often turned in times of stress. Unfortunately, he had a stroke about the same time I did and was unable to see me. His office sent an associate of his. She worked with me daily and gave new meaning to the word "DISLIKE!"

She pushed, she prodded, she belittled me. She was condescending, patronizing...and she was too small in stature to be so arrogant!

One day I said, "I have a question, Doctor. Are you a psychiatrist because you know all the answers?"

She said, "I hope so, do you have a question?"

I answered, "Yes, why does a big girl like you, bite your fingernails?"

She didn't answer my question AND I never saw her again!

MORNING TO EVENING

Morning comes and morning goes
the day begins.
Morning comes and morning goes
the day creeps by.
You never call,
you never come.
Now evening comes and evening goes.
I'm still here,
but all alone.

Sometimes people disappoint you
but you just have to let it go…
and love them anyway.

MARGARET

As the days went by I knew I was losing ground. My doctor suggested I should be moved to our home in Southern California. I was delighted to see my house again. The garden and pool were beautiful but they didn't really stimulate or kindle my old enthusiasm. It seemed a defeat — I retreated into my own safe little world.

After a week or two at home the depression increased. My doctors decided to hospitalize me in Eisenhower Medical Hospital for testing and observation. My condition worsened rapidly.

While there I developed a bad case of gastroenteritis so nurses were ordered 'round the clock

All the usual tests were done, X-rays followed — then medications were changed.

As the gastroenteritis subsided, I spoke with the doctors about going home. They said it would be a good move if I took a nurse with me. It was noticeable that the small progress I had made toward stroke recovery had slipped so it was wise that I have a Registered Nurse.

I knew of the three nurses I had at Eisenhower, I liked Margaret the best. She had a great sense of humor, was very kind and so patient. When it was time for me to leave the hospital, I asked her to go home with me where I would need only one nurse.

Margaret spent the next few days observing me in my own setting; watching over my diet, my habits, my likes and dislikes, and my household, as she considered what changes were necessary.

She insisted I start using a cane with assistance rather than spend so much time in the wheelchair. Margaret walked me down one side of the pool because I was afraid I would fall into the water — imagine! — my own pool that I had been swimming in for many years — I was afraid??

She said, "Don't worry, I'll walk next to the edge. I won't let you fall in." That seemed to pacify me, not knowing then that Margaret had never learned to swim. We walked one half lap at first, gradually increasing to two laps.

Catching a ball became a big part of my day. It started when one of my dogs brought me a tennis ball that he had found. Margaret and I were resting from walking and as I took the ball, it rolled across the game table to her. She, laughing, rolled it back to me. I then bounced it to her and she returned it to me with another bounce. It became a fun game to look forward to daily, but never too long to be tiring.

However, in two weeks we were standing in the back yard, far apart, playing catch as we had with our sons when they were young. Because of the constant repetition I was regaining my strength and coordination. Being a natural athlete this was encouraging and gave me great satisfaction.

CLEANING THE DRAWERS

$\mathcal{L}$et me tell you about the day we cleaned the drawers.

I was in bed that day and in reaching for my bedside table to get my nail file, I brushed aside many scraps of papers and backs of envelopes with scribbles on them.

Margaret asked, "What are all these doing in here?"

I responded, "I write some poetry now and then — when I'm in the mood."

She said, "Well then, let's clean them up — let's straighten up the drawer." She read some of them as we worked. She liked them.

"I don't think you should be throwing these away," she said. "Why don't you print them and give them to your family and friends because I think they are good."

So that's how it began! We started collecting bits and scraps of my poetry and gathering them all together. Then we began cleaning out other drawers. In order to clean the drawers, my brain had to work, my hands had to work, and even my "poor bird" left hand tried to get into the act.

Over a period of a week or so we cleaned 15 drawers. I felt my first sense of accomplishment. I had a new interest in life again. I began to read. I began to think and incidentally, rewrite as I read my own work.

My brain, and my muscles, were functioning again. I began to feel a sense of happiness. I began to think that maybe, one day, there might be a book. It whet my appetite to write again.

MARGARET:

*D*ode was so impatient. We all realized why — she had been through a lot in her life! She is still impatient. But her persistence paid off. Being a perfectionist, if she thinks she can do it, she will do it!"

"She liked her nurses and was willing to cooperate. We can rehabilitate our patients by showing them 'how', but they must 'do' the work themselves. This brings them self-gratification and a feeling of accomplishment and well being.

"For the work Dode did, I introduced new exercises. Her main one was to walk and this was started slowly with a few blocks a day then built up to longer walks and finally small hill climbing.

"I know she complained with, 'I kicked a rock the whole way!' but the results were clearly visible to both of us as well as giving her a feeling of getting back to her usual activity. Because of all this constant repetition she was regaining her strength and her coordination."

PROGRESS!

Learning to Drive Again

"You'd better get in the car today so you can learn to drive, again."

I was ready. We drove in a protected area, away from all traffic. I felt good.

Margaret said later, "Now, see that wasn't so hard." The next day we went to the store. Anybody can drive a Buick!

Back to Church

Margaret was the first one to say to me, "When you go back to Portland, go back to your church. You are an Episcopalian and that's where you belong to worship God."

That was a great recovery step. It had been many months since I had received communion. I can't describe how good I felt at being back in my church with God's hand on my shoulder.

I was reminded: Don't ever doubt that the Lord is with you. He hasn't given up on you so you shouldn't leave Him either.

PROJECTING

You told me about the beauty and the stillness.
How we could walk through the tall trees soundlessly
because of the carpet of pine needles
beneath our feet.

You remembered the colors in the lake were incredible.
Impossible to describe!
You said when I saw them myself I would find words
to portray Nature's work of art.

Your eyes became alive, your breath quickened,
your arms tightened around me
as you told of all the
wonders of your world that I would soon experience.

My heart skipped a beat.
Your recall was so vivid I had a sense
of seeing and touching everything you loved so.
You told me you wanted me to live the dreams along with you.
Ahhh…that, my dear is what I plan to do.

43

THE GENTLE RAIN

The gentle rain,
making a soft patter
on the leaves of the maple tree,
promise a respite
from the searing heat.

The eaves along the roof
have lovely diamond
beads of water,
proving it has been
a steady beat.

Birds sing while
bathing in a puddle.
Flowers lift their heads again.
And neighbors smile and wave
at those they greet.

This was a gift to enjoy
Not an angry storm of
thunder — high winds — destruction.
But a pleasing way in which Nature
renews our faith.

GOOD MORNING!

It's morning…
And the first stirrings of the day begin.
The sky brightens
with a streak of crimson as intense
as the sunset of the night before.
The crows herald the dawn with their raucous caws.
The other birds sleep in a little longer…waiting…
there will be a whole day to sing about.
A whistle blows from a distant train,
wheels clacking on the tracks.
A dog barks, another one answers.
The ducks quietly slip into the pond…
respite from a hot night.
The sky lightens, and more birds
join in the performance,
creating a morning symphony.
Even the bees sleepily buzz their way from blossom to blossom
as the sun begins to warm.
The day has begun…Good morning!

YOUR SMILE

I watch the surprise
in your eyes
as I stroll toward you.
You didn't expect me to walk.

Your smile
is like the sun
breaking through a thunderstorm.
You smile as I take your hand
and life begins anew.

Book Two

THE ROAD BACK

FATHER IN HEAVEN

I walked so long in someone else's shadow — that this is a new life now, a new beginning, a sudden awakening.

Please God, don't let me lose it now. Allow me to savor it a little longer. Let me do for others what I had planned; all the little thoughtful things that I intended to do but never found the time. Please give me that precious time now, that I may lay lie to what Mother used to say, "Dodo, Hell is paved with your good intentions!"

Let me bring love, support and happiness to those I pray for that they may "See your good works and glorify your Father who is in Heaven."

In Jesus name. Amen.

SPLENDOR OF THE MOMENT

The night was soft
the brook was but a gentle murmur.
The clouds parted
and moonlight streamed over us where we lay.
The breeze whispered in the trees
touching my face like a song.
Your lips were close
so I kissed them,
feeling
The splendor of the moment.

CALL ME IRRESISTIBLE

My name is not Betty.
Not today, anyway.
I'm not short and fat and fussy
Appearing for all the world, a hussy.

My name is not Shelley.
Not today, any way.
Tall, flat and spindly — not my bag.
You'll never find me like that hag.

My name is not Susie.
Not today, anyway.
She's all for show — makes quite a display
With all her posturing in frippery array.

My hair's not dyed blonde nor red,
It's always tousled when I'm in bed.
Men tell me I'm lovable, sparkling and charming,
Yet your attitude is but short of alarming.

You can't remember my name!!

LYRIC

As the clouds reflect
the golden sunset…
As the brook echoes
each waterfall…
So, the song of the meadowlark
sounds in my ear.

All these bring thoughts of you.

As we look to the sky
I hear your laugh…
As you allow me to share
a flight to the moon…
So, the waves of the ocean
roar to the shore.

All these bring thoughts of you.

As we walk through leaves
of red and gold…
As a nip in the air
means snow…
So, what does it matter
where we go.

My heart and I agree
you're all the world to me.

HOW DO YOU SPIN THE WORLD?

How can you do exciting, daring, exquisite things
If you are held down by mundane chores
How do you spin the world?
White whales cannot be captured
If one stops to clean up one's room
Or tidy one's desk.

LOVELY LIFE

Life is lovely again.
I noticed the fragrance of the blossoms
as I drove through the orchard.
Also, the intense blue of the sky
reflecting that same color of the water in the lake.
A soft summer breeze
becalms the bees
as poppies nod their heavy heads.
Contentment fills our hearts,
joyous smiles light up our eyes.
Because you are back.

LIVE IT UP

I didn't want to let you go tonight,
I wonder if you've found somebody right.
Don't think you can be single long.
Seeing you alone would be all wrong.

But I've passed my prime.
Just a victim of time.
So you play the field,
I give up; I yield.

Ride your horses — play golf courses,
 from here to there, with friends to spare.
Sail the seas, feel the breeze
blow through your hair.
Fly the skies — and with some surprise
see sun and moon
as they each one rise.
Live it up, darling!
I wish you love.

MY TREASURE

Do you have a rainbow?
I do.
A lovely one with colors.
Borrowed from you.
The blue of your eyes,
Your hair like wheat waving in the wind.
Your radiant smile, accenting
the rosy glow of your being;

Alive with enchantment.

This is my rainbow…
This is my treasure.

PRAYER

A description of an intercessory prayer...
"He prayed as He breathed; forming no words and
making no specific requests, only holding in His heart like broken
birds in cupped hands, all those people who were in stress or grief."
Not unto us, oh Lord. Not unto us, but unto thy Name give praise;
for thy loving mercy, and for thy truths sake.

Amen.

LET IT COME

Have we been together too long?
Do we know each other too well,
    Have we become a habit
    not a joy?

How did we lose it?
Where did it go?
    Was it a gradual thing,
    will we ever know?

I can't always be right
though I think it so.
    And that drives you crazy,
    I know…I know.

Let me hold you again.
Don't call me "Silly girl."
    I still love you, don't mock it.
    Let it come…please.
    Don't knock it!

IT'S OVER

A love affair is over, when it's over —
And it's over.
I leaned to your side of the bed as I turned to get up.
It was empty —
So was I.
I could only think of;

> All the many years when I had rolled over to see your grin,
> Feel your arms around my neck,
> Hear your words,"Hi you",
> Making the morning come alive with your kiss.
> Do you remember how much brighter the days dawned
> When we spent the nights together?
> I do.
> I miss you.
> Miss your smiles —
> They begin in your eyes, you know —
> And touch my heart.
> Touch my heart as words can never do.

I walked out into the ocean breeze,
Crossed the cold sand, down to the lonely sea.
The waves were gentle, but coaxing as they kissed my toes.
I pulled back roughly, thinking I heard your laugh,
Your deep down laughter at my fear of the water.

Sometimes you need the edge to show you where you stand.
And I stand alone!

HIDDEN WELL

My life will ever be just mine to know.
Have I loved too much
or, too many to tell?
I hide it well.
Music brings back memories.
Sights and sounds
are like the ringing of a bell.
But, I hide it well,
With smiles, calm, fun and laughter.
Stories to speak, pictures to paint,
songs to sing forever after.
There's part of me left in everyone I've loved.
And in me a part of them.
Some joy — some Hell.
Yes, I hide it well.

It's only inside that I cry.

PRAYER GROUP

What a pretty face!
But it's hurting…jaws tight,
moist eyes downcast
so we can't see them as you talk.
Your wry smile hides the pain you feel.
But that's why you are here…
This is where you come to unburden
a plate too full.
Just be glad we're on hand to intercede,
to talk with God and receive
His Love for you.

CELEBRATE

I see in your eyes the sadness
of a thousand goodbyes.
And, I hurt for you.
I feel in my heart
the pain that is part of your loneliness.
And, I hurt for you.
But, I hear in your voice
To have faith ... to rejoice!
And, I have love for you.
One God, world without end. Amen

AFTER YOU'D GONE

After you'd gone,
I went back to your room
Cold as a tomb
In it's emptiness.

After you'd gone,
Bus token in a drawer — little more.
It said, ONE FARE.
But to where?

I never asked when you went away,
You didn't say.
Maybe that's what went wrong
Along the way.

After you'd gone
There was no one to care, to share.
Life was bare.
There was nothing you left
But me…

'S ENOUGH!

You should be happy —
I love you as you wish.
No demands,
No expectations,
You owe me nothing.
I have memories of
Our days of loving.
And extraordinary recall.
'S enough!

ADIOS

It finally came…
Goodbye!
I knew it when you pushed your food around
on your dinner plate…
then lighted a cigarette after
six months of not touching them.

You slowly walked away outside the Inn.
Your shoulders drooped in the hot still night…
Just a lazy wave of your hand,
no looking back.
Nothing to be said…when it's over,
it's over…
G'bye!

THE PARDON

So, I've lived a different life,
Not the one You advocate.
Skipped the prayers I used to say,
Even church on Easter Day.
     What went wrong along the way?
     Could I come back to You, someday?

Did my friends become a crowd?
Were they all too lax and loud?
Did You frown to find them free?
Forever on their spree; and not at all like me.
     What went wrong along the way?
     May I come back to You, someday?

Every foot has seemed a mile,
Every joke just not my style,
Nor the conduct You have asked from me.
Now it's time to listen, look and see.
     May I come back to You, today?

It's "Welcome" in Your gentle smile.
Forgiveness in Your eyes.
Your arms will always open wide
To hold me, pardoned, by Your side.

HOT NIGHT

The night is hot, still and humid. You lie sweating on your rumpled bed by the open window, listening to sounds that echo down through the steamy alley.

A baby's cry.

Dance hall jazz, the slow moan of a clarinet.

Cats mating.

Screeching brakes, a horn honking,

The wail of a siren.

Drunks singing as they stagger to the next bar.

The couple upstairs…he hit her again, she's sobbing.

And all you feel is tired, burned out, alone, forsaken, and ohhh… so damned hot.

Can't go back…who'd want you…nobody now!

That's what she said.

Don't worry, Angel, I'll never return from this trip…

Heart stumbling, head pounding, ears screaming, eyes tearing, body aching and soaking wet.

G'bye…

Remember,

we loved each other…once.

I - ME - MYSELF - MINE

No one could feel your presence at all times, in all ways,
as I do Lord — as I have since childhood —
You were always there!

Please rid me of the ingrained selfishness I struggle with.
Me - Myself - Mine —

Steep those thoughts for others;
Their troubles, their problems, their health, wants,
families, their desires —

Help me to give even more than I receive from each
relationship or each church service.

To hear the prayers others ask and offer.
To hear the gospel — really hear!

God give me love
And God give me patience.

MOTHERS

In an instant, winter's embrace
cut her gentle trace
to my soul, once again.
Little at a time the chilling caress captures
Each pore of my skin
and the cold of Mother Nature
Takes me back to my childhood.

"Dress warm now. Button your coat.
Be sure to wear a hat. Don't lose your mittens.
Yes, you have to wear your overshoes."
Moms are like that because
Their Moms were like that
Because their Moms were like
That because…

WINTER

Coat collars up, gloves and boots on.
Slickers, a must for the day.
Cold wind is a-sharpnin' to a blast.
The rain has turned to sleet... and;
Winter is a-comin' in but fast.

Snow will soon weigh down the boughs.
Drifts will cover paths.
Phone lines are a-pullin' on their mast.
The pond is icin' up... yeah;
Winter is a-comin' in but fast.

Need extra quilts of down upon the bed.
With Long-Johns day and night.
If this be any sign of seasons past,
We'd best get ready now... 'cause'
Winter is a-comin in but fast.

Aren't you glad you have me to take care of you?

CIRCUS DAYS

It was fun
when we were young…
remember?
The popcorn smelled so good!
The hot dogs were great…
but the mustard was greater.

The clowns with their frightful wigs,
painted faces,
baggy pants held up by braces,
made us laugh
'til we cried.
If they had any pride,
must have been inside.

But my favorite was the carrousel
and me astride a swiftly running horse...
it's plaster nostrils flaring, mane flying...
racing to win;
amid bright lights and mirrors,
the tinny music sounding a rousing din.

The beat of the drum,
the blare of the trumpets,
Added sparkle to costumes…and
Spice to the tigers
prowling back and forth
in their red wagons.

It was fun
when we were young!

THE NEARNESS OF GOD

We place our belief in God
Who is at all times, everywhere present.
In the people around us
We see His presence…
    in a warm smile,
    a friendly hug,
    a thoughtful comment.
There is no break
In the oneness of us.
God is with you as He is with me.
He holds each of us in His loving hands
To grow closer to unity…
    closer to caring,
    closer to sharing
the loving vibrant presence of God.

JUST PLAIN HELL

Just when I've found you
I lose you.
Just when I learn to smile
I cry.
Easy — ? Whoever said it was easy?
This caring, this sharing,
This giving, this living
Alone.
It's just plain Hell!

Just when I need you
You leave me.
Just when I wait
You don't show.
Easy — ? I never said it was easy!
This hoping, this coping,
This longing, prolonging this
Loneliness.
It's just plain Hell!

There must be a way
You'll come home to stay.
If there's something I lack
I'll get back on the track,
And promise never to stray.

Just when I see you
Still love me,
That's when I'll sing again —
Or try —
Easy, — I always said it was easy!
The caring, and sharing,
And giving, and living
Together —
It's just plain Paradise.

KNOW THYSELF

A friend told me today that I must never lose my identity.
        "You must always remember from where you came;
            where you are going and who is with you at all times to
            point the way, applauding your achievements.
            You have to know that it is not going to fall apart
            if you invest yourself."
This is my strength, — a gift from God.

SOLD

The snow laden mountains peek
from behind the darker foremost hills.
I happily hum as
I rapidly walk toward these
and the sounds of the city recede
to those of this;
our hidden retreat, deep in the woods.
A lazy creek, a gentle waterfall,
chirping birds, rustling leaves,
the life in this Paradise begins to stir.
I raise my voice in resounding song.

The cranky owl, one eye closed,
looks down from his lofty perch.
He doesn't give a hoot about my excitement.
The little grey squirrel hungrily munches
his lunches.

The carpet of pine needles beneath my feet
is soft, my steps almost silent.
I hurry lest I keep you waiting,
knowing full well you are always late.
But today is special and perhaps you will be on time.

As you round the bend I burst out
with such a shout
the owl opens his other eye,
the squirrel drops his lunch.
And when you spread your arms to me…
I know that you know…

They Bought It … They Bought My Book!

RECOVERED

Now I can run with you.
Play games with you,
eat and drink with you.

And when you come to me
We can rejoice in our laughter.
I can still soothe you
when you are troubled…

Still teach you all I have learned,
Because now I am whole again.
And we are together.